Spookyrumpus

For Rosa and Trudi ~ T.M.

For Sian and Laura
and special thanks for the Goldy magic ~ G.P.R.

Orchard Books
Carmelite House, 50 Victoria Embankment, London EC4Y 0DZ
Orchard Books Australia
Level 17/207 Kent Street, Sydney, NSW 2000
ISBN 978 1 40835 035 5
First published in 2004 by Orchard Books
First published in paperback in 2005
Text © Tony Mitton 2004
Illustrations © Guy Parker-Rees 2004
The rights of Tony Mitton to be identified as the author
and Guy Parker-Rees to be identified as the illustrator
of this work have been asserted by them in accordance
with the Copyright, Designs and Patents Act, 1988.
A CIP catalogue record for this book is available
from the British Library.
Printed in China
Orchard Books is a division of Hachette Children's Books,
an Hachette UK company
www.hachette.co.uk

Spookyrumpus

Tony Mitton

Guy Parker-Rees

ORCHARD

BONG! goes the bell in the rickety tower,
Twelve times...that means it's Spooky Hour.

Listen! Hush! Oooh, what's that sound?
The midnight spooks are coming round.

Then off they zoom on broomsticks, wheeeeee!

Out of the darkness, what's this here?

Ten funny, floaty ghosts appear,

Swirling, whirling, singing, "Whoo-ooooo!

Watch out, witches. We're after you-ooooooo!"

Nine skeletons dance by, clickety-clack.
Their snapping teeth go snickety-snack.

At the edge of the trees, tu-whit tu-whoo,
Eight spooky owls hoot, "We'll come too."

Leaping high and creeping low,

Seven scary cats with eyes that glow!

From deep in the wood comes a rumbling sound,

And what's that scuttling?

Better be wary…

Five big spiders, fat and hairy.

Shadows leap as your heart beats quicker.
Through the trees comes a splutter and flicker.

Four wizards, holding lanterns bright,
Go by in dancing candlelight.

Beside the gate to the castle yard,
Three suits of armour stand on guard.

A noise comes swirling down the stair.

Let's go on up. Oh, do we dare?

"Cackle cackle...tee-hee-hee..."

I wonder who that is?

Let's see...

rise!"

two big grins,

Are Mitch and Titch,

the witchy twins.

And what's this here?

Oh me, oh my!

It's...

Then Mitch says, "Come on, everyone. Let's have some scary party fun!"

They hide away
in funny places,
Then pop out,
BOO!
with spooky faces.

They leap and swirl,
they howl and shriek,
As they play at screechy
hide-and-seek.

But even spooks can have enough,
And in the end, they're out of puff.

As the morning sun begins to rise,
They start to yawn and rub their eyes.

They stretch,
and scratch
their sleepy heads...

Then home they go to snuggly beds.